GW00535710

STARTING TO COUNT

Jenny Tyler and Robyn Gee

Designed and illustrated by Graham Round

With consultant advice from John Newson and Gillian Hartley
of the Child Development Research Unit at Nottingham University.

About this book

This book is for an adult and child to use together and is designed to
help a young child's understanding of numbers.

The first pages introduce the numbers one to five and contain
activities which concentrate on counting and on recognizing and
writing these numbers. More varied activities on the pages that
follow will then increase the child's familiarity and confidence in
dealing with the numbers up to five.

Towards the end of the book, the range of questions and activities is
widened to introduce the ideas that numbers can be arranged in a
logical sequence, that sets of the same size can be matched and
that numbers can be combined to form other numbers.

Notes for parents

It is best to use this book when both you and your child are in the right mood to enjoy it. Try not to do too much at any one time and if the child seems unready or unwilling to tackle any of the activities, just leave it and come back to it later. Short frequent sessions, perhaps followed up by some counting activities of your own, will allow the child's concentration span to develop gradually.

Pens and pencils

You will need a set of crayons or felt pens for the colouring activities in this book. These could also be used for the drawing and writing activities, though you may prefer to choose a pencil for these. Whatever you choose, before you start, check that your child is holding it correctly. It is easy to develop bad writing habits with the wrong grip.

Pens and pencils should be held between the thumb and first two fingers, about 2 cm from the point, and not gripped too tightly.

Make the most of all the colouring opportunities offered by each page, not all of them have been specifically mentioned. Besides being enjoyable and satisfying, colouring helps to develop pencil control.

Each page also offers plenty of counting opportunities other than those mentioned; and simply talking about pictures together helps to develop powers of observation and increase vocabulary.

About learning to count

Learning to count is a gradual process which is helped by repetition and practice. You can help your child to become familiar with number names and their sequence by singing number songs and rhymes and by counting objects and events with them, such the steps as you go up or down stairs. A child may be able to recite numbers, though, before being able to count properly and needs to understand that in counting, each number refers to only one object or action.

You can help at this stage by matching one object to one other appropriate object or person. (This is sometimes referred to as "one-to-one correspondence".) For example you could get your child to count how many people will be sitting down for a meal and then let him help put out the right number of forks, spoons, plates and so on.

You can give children further practice by counting things in their daily experience, such as toys, cups, biscuits and so on; and by pointing out numbers in their everyday environment, such as house numbers, bus numbers and car number plates.

Early counting may be helped if you count small objects which can be picked up and moved as you say the relevant number. This emphasises the procedure of counting and discourages the child from racing through the numbers in a meaningless way. You could also label containers with different numbers and help the child to count in the correct number of small objects, such as buttons.

Any games that involve numbers and counting, such as dominoes and simple board games will also help make learning to count fun for your child.

one

I jelly

I ↓

- Colour the jelly.

- Find I frog and colour it.

- Draw I ball.

- How many spoons can you see?

- How many bowls can you see?

- Colour the number one red.

I   2   3   4   5

2 two

2 paper cups

2 2 2 2 2 2

- Colour the paper cups.

- Find 2 frogs and colour them.

- Draw 2 balls.

- How many straws can you see?

- How many party hats can you find?

- Colour the number two blue.

1   2   3   4   5

3 three

3 birthday presents

3

- Colour the birthday presents.

- Find 3 frogs to colour.

- Draw 3 balls.

- How many labels can you see?

- How many cards are there?

- Colour the number three green.

4 four

4 candles

4

- Colour the candles.

- Find 4 frogs to colour.

- Draw 4 balls.

- How many stars are there on the cake?

- How many knives can you find?

- Colour the number four yellow.

1 2 3 4 5

5 five

5 cakes

5 5 5 5 5 5

- Colour the cakes.

- Find 5 frogs to colour.

- Draw 5 balls.

- How many cherries can you see? ☐

- How many silver balls can you find? ☐

- Colour the number five orange.

1 2 3 4 5

1 2 3 4 5

- How many crackers can you see?
- Colour them in.

- Colour the candles.
- How many are there?

- How many jellies are there?

- Colour the birthday presents.
- How many can you find?

- How many paper cups are there?
- Colour them in.

- How many little cakes can you find to colour?

- How many frogs can you find?
- Colour them in.

1   2   3   4   5

| 1 | | | 4 | |

- Write the missing numbers in the boxes.

9

• Write the numbers in the boxes.

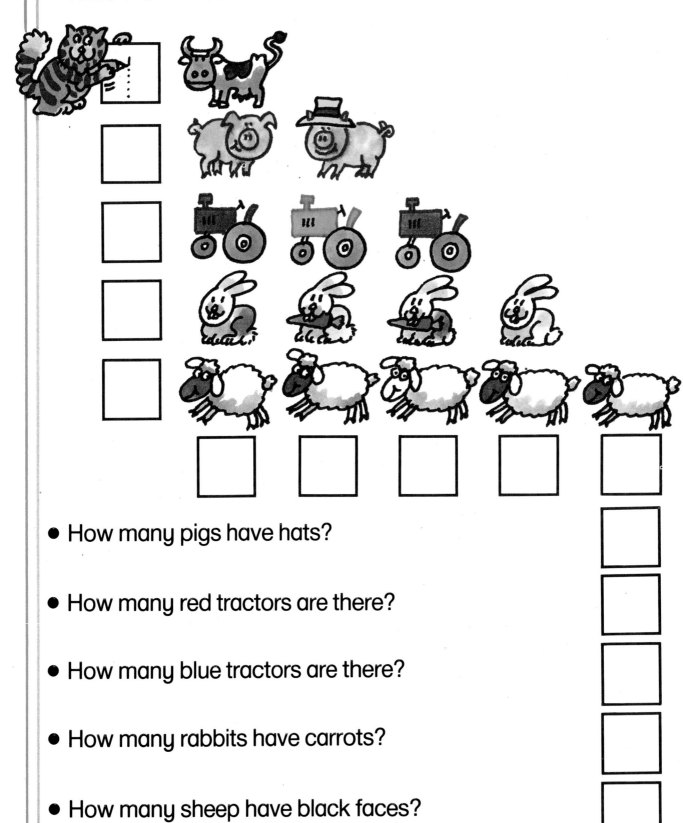

• How many pigs have hats?

• How many red tractors are there?

• How many blue tractors are there?

• How many rabbits have carrots?

• How many sheep have black faces?

- How many animals are there in the field? ☐
- Draw I tail on each animal.

- How many hens can you see? ☐
- Draw 2 eggs under each hen.

- How many ducks are swimming on the pond? ☐

- Draw 2 more ducks.
- How many ducks are there now? ☐

11

1 2 3 4 5

- How many spiders can you find? ☐

- Colour 2 butterflies.

- How many snails can you find? ☐

- Colour the 3-spot ladybirds red.

- Colour the 1-spot ladybirds yellow.

- How many bees can you find? ☐

- How many bees are flying in the air? ☐

- Colour 2 caterpillars.

- How many petals on each pink flower? ☐

- Colour 3 butterflies.

- Match the pairs of socks and draw a line to join them.

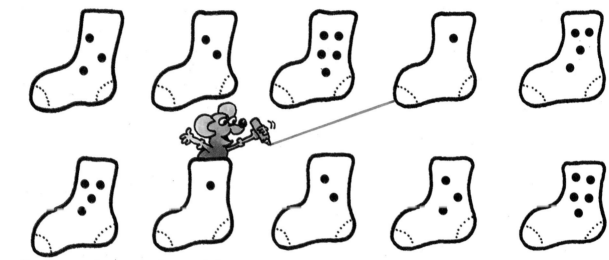

- Colour the socks with:

4 spots red   I spot yellow   3 spots pink

5 spots blue   2 spots green

- Match each T-shirt with its pair of shorts.
- Draw a line to join them.
- Colour each T-shirt to match its shorts.

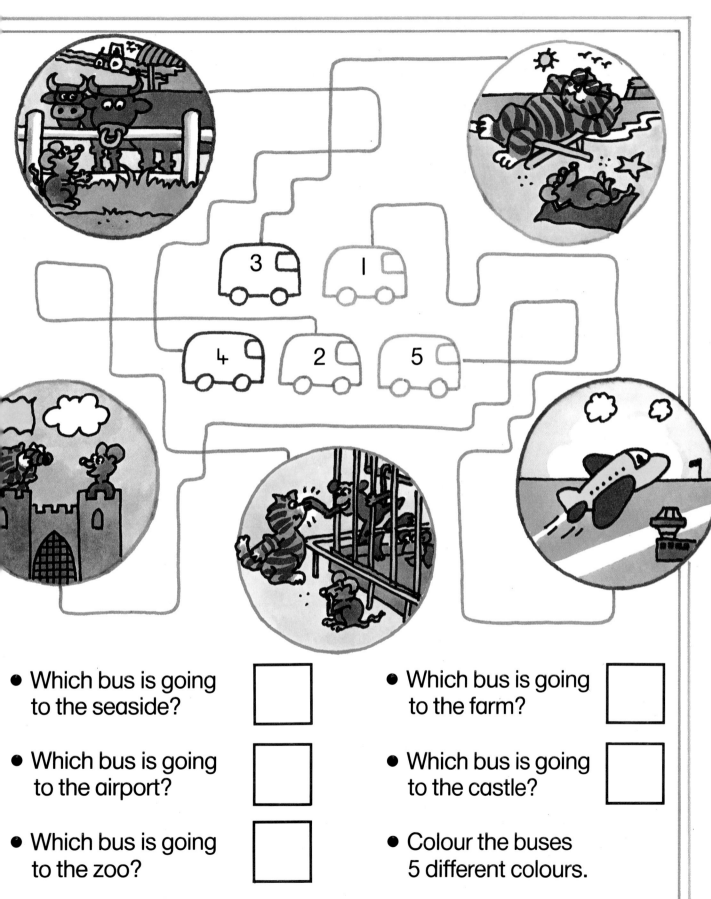

2 3 4 5

- Which bus is going to the seaside? ☐

- Which bus is going to the airport? ☐

- Which bus is going to the zoo? ☐

- Which bus is going to the farm? ☐

- Which bus is going to the castle? ☐

- Colour the buses 5 different colours.

15

1 2 3 4 5

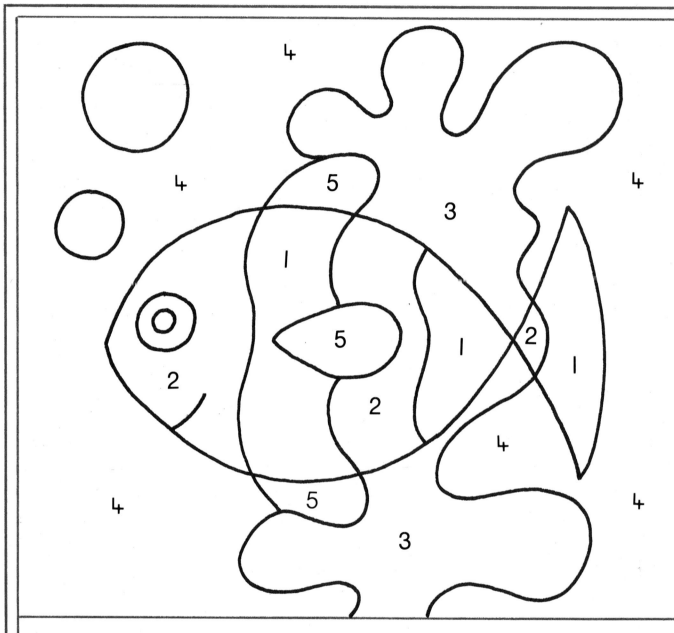

- Colour the picture. The numbers tell you which colours to use. What is in the picture?

1 red

2 yellow

3 green

4 blue

5 black

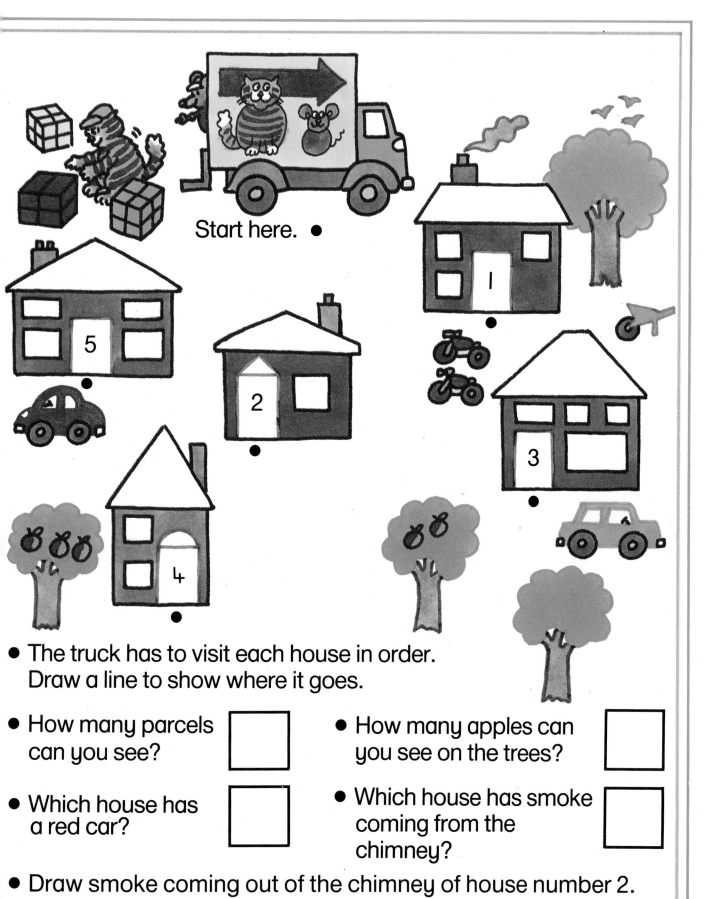

Start here.

- The truck has to visit each house in order.
  Draw a line to show where it goes.

- How many parcels can you see? ☐

- How many apples can you see on the trees? ☐

- Which house has a red car? ☐

- Which house has smoke coming from the chimney? ☐

- Draw smoke coming out of the chimney of house number 2.

1 2 3 4 5

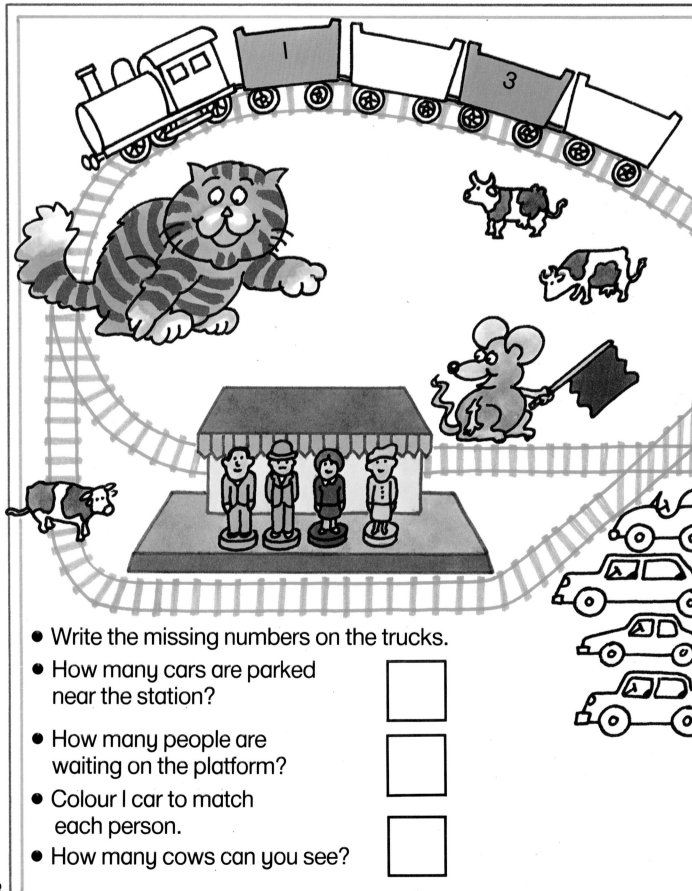

- Write the missing numbers on the trucks.
- How many cars are parked near the station?
- How many people are waiting on the platform?
- Colour 1 car to match each person.
- How many cows can you see?

- How many trees are there? ☐

- How many trees have fallen down? ☐

- How many frogs can you find to colour? ☐

- Write the numbers of the trucks with frogs in them?

☐ ☐ ☐

- Colour the engines.

1 2 3 4 5

- How many clouds? ☐
- Colour 2 clouds grey.
- Colour 2 umbrellas blue.
- Colour 2 umbrellas red.
- How many umbrellas are there altogether? ☐

- How many raindrops can you see? ☐
- Colour 2 raindrops blue.
- Colour 1 aeroplane.
- How many aeroplanes are left? ☐

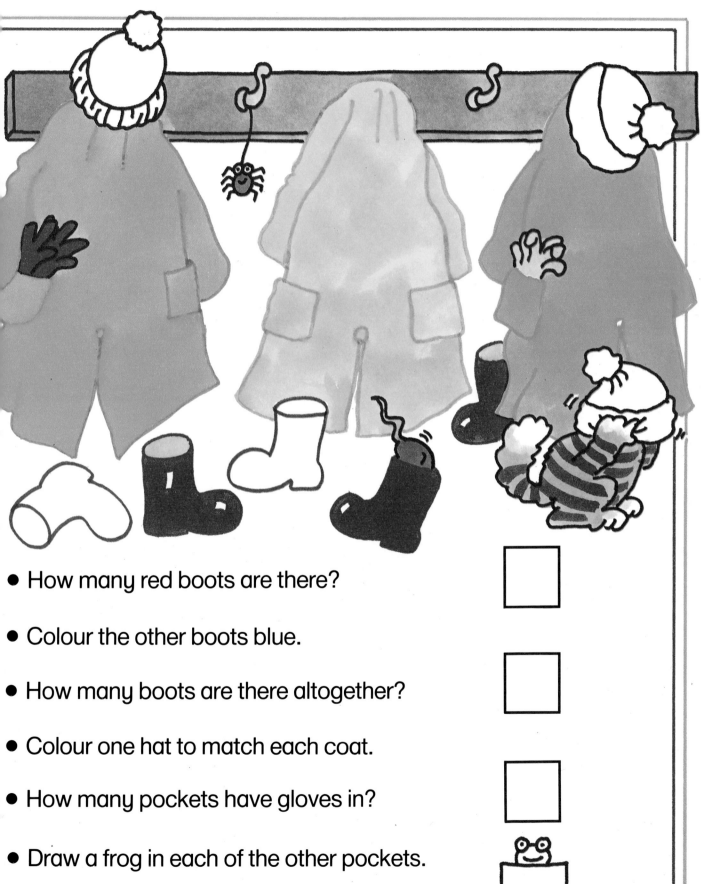

- How many red boots are there?

- Colour the other boots blue.

- How many boots are there altogether?

- Colour one hat to match each coat.

- How many pockets have gloves in?

- Draw a frog in each of the other pockets.

1 2 3 4 5

- Each set of mice has its own plate of cheese.
- Draw a line from each set of mice to its plate of cheese.

- Write down the number of mice in the box under each set.

- Count the sweets in each jar.
- Join the strings to show which label belongs to each jar.

- How many sweets has the mouse got?
- How many sweets has the cat got?

- Put a circle around the one who has more.

- Draw sweets in each jar to match the number on the label.

23

1 2 3 4 5

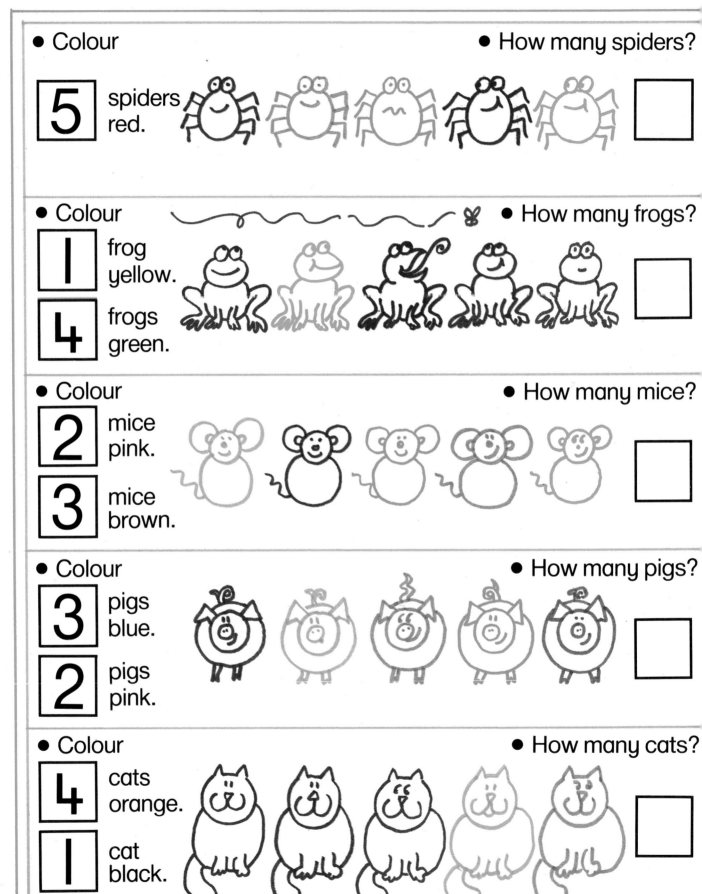

- Colour

  | 5 | spiders red. |

  - How many spiders?

- Colour

  | 1 | frog yellow. |
  | 4 | frogs green. |

  - How many frogs?

- Colour

  | 2 | mice pink. |
  | 3 | mice brown. |

  - How many mice?

- Colour

  | 3 | pigs blue. |
  | 2 | pigs pink. |

  - How many pigs?

- Colour

  | 4 | cats orange. |
  | 1 | cat black. |

  - How many cats?